# 1 What is "microelectronics"?

## Information: Microelectr

At the heart of microelectronics is the **silicon chip**. The chip has made a tremendous impact on the way we live and it is probably the most important invention this century.

Everybody has benefitted in some way, from the way we make things to the way we relax. The chip has reduced the size of computers from the size of a large room to the size of a book. It has made possible robots, video games, calculators, programmable washing-machines, hospital equipment . . . the list goes on and on.

A silicon chip is a small slice of a material called **silicon**, about the size of a pea. On its surface it carries not just one or two but hundreds of electronic devices through which tiny signals flow. Because so much electronics is packed into such a small area it is called **microelectronics**.
The number of electronic circuits that chips can carry is increasing all the time.

The picture shows electronic devices joined by wires and copper tracks to make an **electronic circuit**. Small electric signals flow through the wires, and the way the devices control these signals is known as **electronics.**

The chips are sealed in plastic cases to protect them.
**Pins** stick out from the sides of the case and these carry the electric signals to and from the chip.

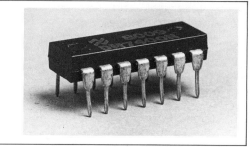

There are many thousands of different chips. In this book you can use a few of them to control the machines that you build.

**Q1** How have we benefitted from microelectronics?

**Q2** What is the difference between electronics and microelectronics?

**Q3** Make a list of all the things that you can think of which have silicon chips inside them.

# 2 Sweet machine

## Building a "Smartie" dispenser

**Apparatus**
LEGO Technical Functions Kit No. 1032      Smarties
solenoid board      ruler

You must have seen machines which give you chocolate bars when you put in your money. These two pages show you how to build a machine which will dispense Smarties. (When you have finished you will need to keep your machine safe for future experiments.)

**A** Start with the green base and fit LEGO pieces as the picture shows.

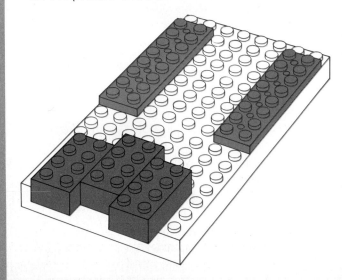

**B**

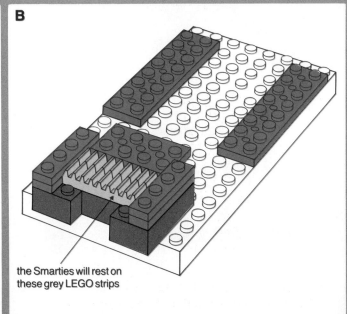

the Smarties will rest on these grey LEGO strips

**C** Add some more pieces . . .

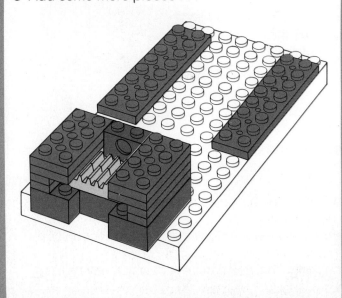

**D**

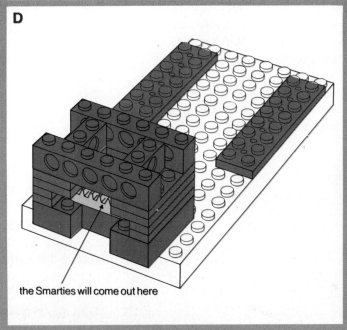

the Smarties will come out here

**2** Sweet machine

**E** Continue adding LEGO pieces to build a container for the Smarties.

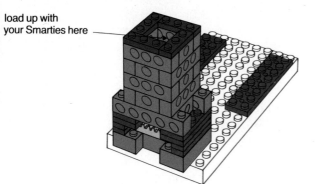

load up with
your Smarties here

**F** You are going to use the solenoid board to push Smarties out of your dispenser.

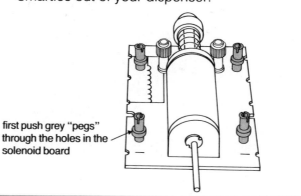

first push grey "pegs"
through the holes in the
solenoid board

**G** Then fasten the solenoid board to your dispenser.

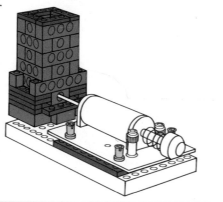

**H** Now turn over your dispenser and fasten "legs" to it.

The legs have different sizes so use the ruler and look at the picture to see where they go.

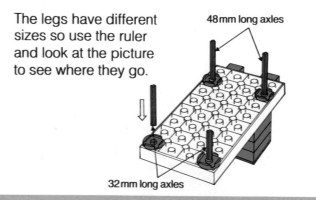

48 mm long axles

32 mm long axles

**I** Your dispenser should look like this.

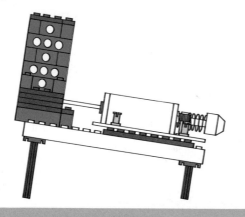

**J** Now carefully load your dispenser with Smarties so that they *lie flat*. You should be able to get ten in.

Then try moving the solenoid forwards and back with your hand.

Watch carefully to find out why only one Smartie comes out each time.

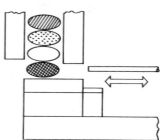

Write the heading "Sweet dispenser" in your book and then draw a diagram to show how it works.

**Q1** How does the dispenser give only one Smartie at a time?

**Q2** Make a list of all the dispensing machines you can think of.

# 3 Controlling your sweet dispenser

## Push-button control system

### Apparatus
6 V battery (or power supply)     your sweet dispenser
2 connecting wires     3 connecting strips     Smarties
Control boards: battery connector (or power supply regulator),
switch unit, transducer driver

The solenoid on your sweet dispenser will move by itself if you connect electricity to it. In this experiment you will be able to get a Smartie just by pressing a push-button.

**A** In all the **control systems** that you will build, the first board to look for is the **battery connector** (or **power supply regulator** if you are using a power pack). This board carries the electricity to your control system.

Don't connect the battery yet.

**B** Use connecting strips to join the control boards together. It is important that you use them the right way round.

always use the connector this way up with the "pip" towards the bottom

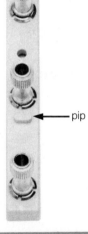

pip

**C** Now connect the **switch unit** to the battery connector. Using the switch unit, you can turn the electricity on and off in your control system.

Push the boards together and then tighten the screw connectors

turn this way to tighten

**D** The switch unit only gives out small amounts of electricity. This is not enough to make the solenoid work. So a **transducer driver** is used to make the electricity from the switch big enough to work the solenoid.

Read on to see how to connect it.

## 3 Controlling your sweet dispenser

**E** Now finish your control system by adding the transducer driver and then connect the solenoid of your sweet dispenser.

Look carefully to see where the wires go.

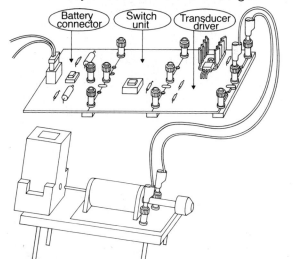

**F** Next connect your battery to the battery connector. (If instead you are using a power pack, connect it to the power supply regulator. Make sure it is set to 12 V and switch on.)

Now press the push-button on the switch unit and see what happens.

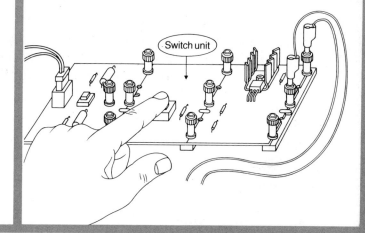

**G** The control system that you have built looks like this:

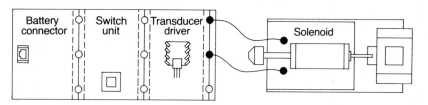

Pictures like this can take a long time to draw. So instead of pictures we will draw **block diagrams** like the one below.

In block diagrams we leave out the power supply.

**H** All control systems have at least one **input** and at least one **output**. In the system you have just built, the switch is the input and the solenoid is the output.

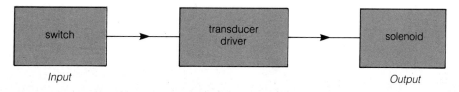

Put the heading "Push-button control system" in your book and then draw a block diagram of your control system.

**Q1** Describe what happens when the push-button is pressed.

**Q2** What is the input and what is the output of your control system?

**3** Controlling your sweet dispenser

# Magnetic switch control system

### Apparatus
6 V battery (or power supply)     your sweet dispenser
LEGO Technical Functions Kit No. 1032     2 connecting wires
3 connecting strips     Smarties     magnet
Control boards: battery connector (or power supply regulator),
remote sensor unit, transducer driver, magnetic switch

Anybody can push the button on your control system to "steal" a Smartie. In this experiment a magnetic switch is used instead of the push-button, so only somebody with a magnet can get your sweets.

**A** The magnetic switch is called a **reed switch.** You must first connect it to the **remote sensor unit** before you can use it in a control system.

The remote sensor unit and the reed switch *together* will form the input of your control system.

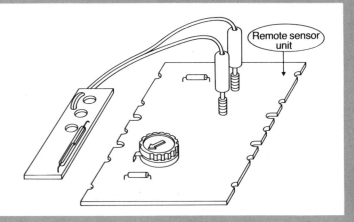

**B** Now fasten the reed switch to your sweet dispenser. Work out the best way of doing it using the LEGO kit.

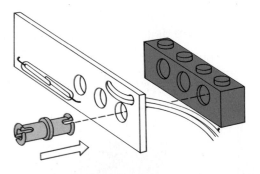

**C** Then build the control system (remember to start with the battery connector)

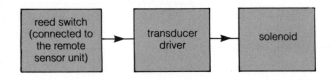

Does it push out a Smartie when you bring a magnet near the reed switch?

Find out which way to hold the magnet for best results.

You could try building LEGO pieces around the reed switch to hide it and then challenge a friend to try to get one of your Smarties (the LEGO bricks won't stop the magnetism).

Put the heading "Magnetic switch control system" in your book and then draw your control system.

**Q3**  What is the input and what is the output of your control system?

# Information: Vending machines

There are many different types of **vending machines** dispensing a wide variety of products, ranging from chocolate and crisps to cigarettes and drinks.

Although there are differences in the way they look and the products they dispense, most vending machines need a **coin handling system.**

This picture shows the inside of the vending machine.

When you put a coin in a vending machine, the coin handling system tests the coin. It tests whether the coin you put in is really a coin and not just a piece of metal. Then it works out the value of the coin.

If the coin fails any of the tests then it is rejected.

There are still some **mechanical** coin handling systems in use but more and more **microelectronics** systems are being used.

Inside the coin handling system, the coin slides down a series of slopes. As it slides, the coin passes different **sensors** which determine the **thickness, material** and **diameter** of the coin.

Some coin handling systems test for the roundness of the coin and even if a string is tied to the coin.

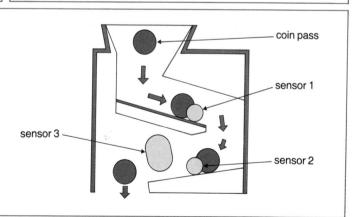

**Q4** What does the coin handling system do?

**Q5** Why is it important to make tests on the coins?

# Light-sensitive control system

**Apparatus**
6 V battery (or power supply)      your sweet dispenser
2 connecting wires     4 connecting strips      Smarties
LEGO Technical Functions Kit No. 1032
Control boards: battery connector (or power supply regulator),
lamp, remote sensor unit, transducer driver, light sensor, inverter

If you use a **light sensor** as the input to your control system, you will be able to get your dispenser to work by shining a light on it.

**A** Plug the light sensor into the remote sensor unit. This is the input of your control system.

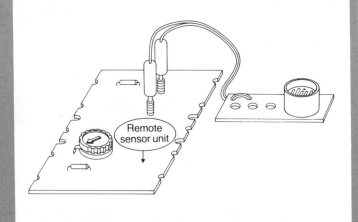

**B** Now fasten the light sensor to the front of your sweet dispenser.

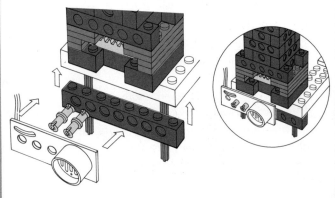

**C** Then build your control system. (Remember to start with the battery connector.)

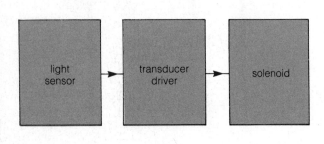

Let's call this control system 1.

**D** You need a light for this experiment so plug in the lamp as the picture shows.

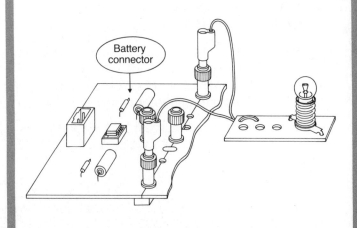

**3** Controlling your sweet dispenser

**E** Now switch on and step by step, turn the control on the remote sensor board.

When the control is in the right position a Smartie will be dispensed each time the light shines on the light sensor.

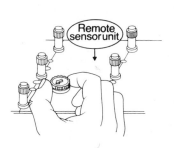

**F** You can change your control system quite easily so that it operates when it gets dark.

First switch off and add the **inverter** to your control system.

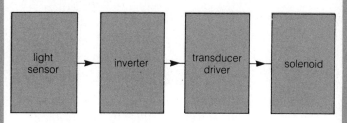

Let's call this control system 2.

**G** Then switch on again and hold the lamp in front of the light sensor about 10 cm away.

Next slowly turn the control on the remote sensor unit until the indicator light on the inverter *just* goes out.

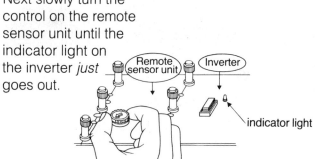

indicator light

**H** Now pass your hand between the lamp and the light sensor.
Did you catch a Smartie?

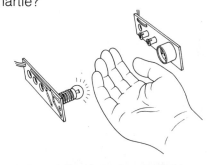

In your book, write the heading "Light-sensitive systems". Then draw diagrams of control system 1 and control system 2 and label them.

**Q6** Which system was operated by darkness?

**Q7** Which system was operated by light?

**Q8** What was added to the control system to change it from a light-operated system to a darkness-operated system?

**Q9** Mary was bothered by her brother who kept teasing her by putting plastic spiders and mice in the drawer of her dressing table. So she decided to set a trap as the picture shows.
a) What sensor did she use in the drawer?
b) Draw the control system she used.

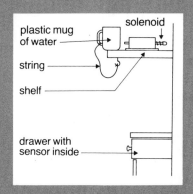

**Q10** Think of some different uses for light-sensitive control systems. There is no need to use a solenoid as the output (a motor or lamp could be used instead). Write down your ideas in your book. How many can you think of?

# Mini Project 1: Automatic box-filling machine

### Apparatus
6 V battery (or power supply)     your sweet dispenser     Smarties
2 connecting wires     4 connecting strips     motor lead
empty matchbox     ruler     LEGO Technical Functions Kit No. 1032
Control boards: battery connector (or power supply regulator),
remote sensor unit, transducer driver, light sensor, lamp, inverter

In this factory bottles are being carried along on a conveyor belt. A sensor detects any bottles without caps, or any gaps in the line of bottles, and stops the production line until the capless bottle is removed or the gap fills up.

You have learnt enough to build your own automatic production line. In this miniproject your machine will automatically put a sweet into a matchbox on a conveyor belt.

**A** First build up the axle supports and push the axles through. Then push the collars and pulleys into place and stretch drive belts over the pulleys. The drive belts will form the conveyor belt in your project.

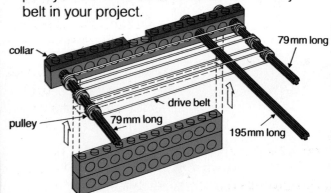

collar
pulley
drive belt
79 mm long
79 mm long
195 mm long

**B** Now build up the supports for the loose ends of the axles.

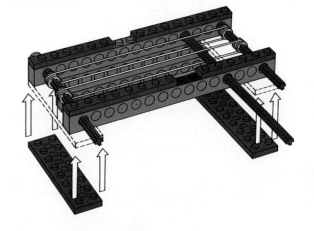

**C** Next add the motor and push on collars to hold the axles.

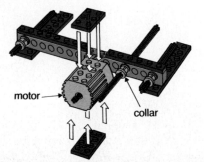

motor
collar

**D** Then push on the pulleys and stretch drive belts over them.

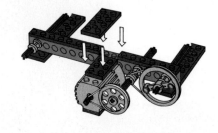

**3** Controlling your sweet dispenser

**E** Remove the front legs from your sweet dispenser and fasten the light sensor to it. Now join the dispenser and conver belt together.

Your machine should look like this:

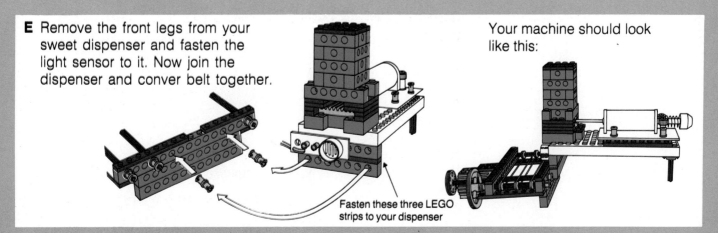

Fasten these three LEGO strips to your dispenser

**F** Fasten the lamp on top of the motor to complete the construction of your machine.

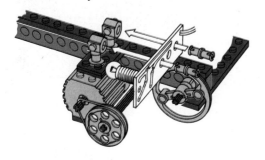

**H** Then plug in the lamp and the lead to your conveyor motor. The picture shows you how to do it.

Now switch on to test the lamp and the conveyor belt. If you find the conveyor goes the wrong way, swap over the motor leads.

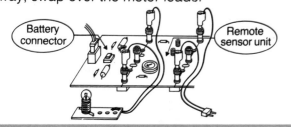

Battery connector

Remote sensor unit

**G** Now let's build the control system.

Remember, the solenoid must work when the matchbox reaches the light sensor. So which control system should you build?

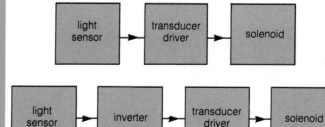

When you have decided build the system but do not switch on yet.

**I** You are ready to try out your machine. Load your dispenser with Smarties and put the matchbox on the conveyor belt. Did the box catch a Smartie?

You may have to adjust the control on the remote sensor unit as you did on page 9.

Adjust your machine until the box catches a Smartie every time.

If you have time, try the "Extra Work". If not, separate your sweet dispenser from the conveyor and put them somewhere safe.

**Extra Work**

You need to join with at least one other group for this.

Put the machines together so that a matchbox will move from one conveyor belt to the next.

Load one dispenser with one colour, the next dispenser with a different colour, and so on. Now try it out.

Did you get a different coloured Smartie from each dispenser?

**3** Controlling your sweet dispenser

# Using an OR gate

### Apparatus
6 V battery (or power supply)      your sweet dispenser      Smarties
3 connecting wires      7 connecting strips
Control boards: battery connector, (or power supply regulator),
2 switch units, an OR gate, power link, transducer driver

With some control systems it is useful to have two inputs. Sometimes we want one input OR the other input to operate the system.

Put the heading "OR gate" in your notebook and copy the table.

| Switch A pressed ? | Switch B pressed ? | Smartie dispensed ? |
|---|---|---|
| no | no | |
| no | yes | |
| yes | no | |
| yes | yes | |

**A** You need to use the power link to supply power to both inputs.

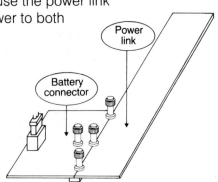

**B** This is the control system you should build.

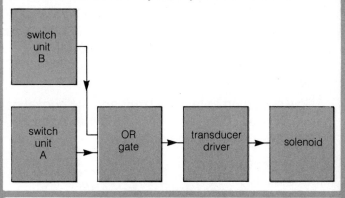

**C** One of the inputs to the OR gate must be joined by a connecting wire.

**D** Try pressing switch A, then switch B, and finally both together. Fill in the table with your results.

# Information: Truth-tables

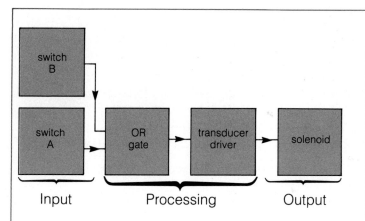

Input   Processing   Output

| Switch A pressed ? | Switch B pressed ? | Sweet dispensed ? |
|---|---|---|
| no | no | no |
| no | yes | yes |
| yes | no | yes |
| yes | yes | yes |

In the last experiment you drew a table showing whether or not a sweet was dispensed when the switches were pressed. This sort of table is useful because it tells you what the output of your system will do when the inputs change.

Electronic engineers use these tables a lot. Often they write a "1" instead of yes and a "0" instead of no. The table is called a **truth-table**.

This is a truth-table for an OR gate.

| Switch A | Switch B | Output |
|---|---|---|
| 0 | 0 | 0 |
| 0 | 1 | 1 |
| 1 | 0 | 1 |
| 1 | 1 | 1 |

Notice that the output is on if either switch A OR switch B is on.

If you change the control system, the truth-table will change.

In between the Input and Output sections of your control system is the **Processing** section. By changing the processing you can make the output behave the way you want it to.

You will learn about different processing ideas as you work through this book.

**Q11** How is a truth-table useful?

**Q12** In a truth-table, what does a "1" mean?

**3** Controlling your sweet dispenser

# Using an AND gate

### Apparatus
6 V battery (or power supply)     your sweet dispenser     Smarties
3 connecting wires     7 connecting strips
Control boards: battery connector (or power supply regulator),
2 switch units, an AND gate, power link, remote sensor unit,
light sensor, transducer driver

Can you guess how the AND gate will be different from the OR gate?

Put the heading "AND gate" in your notebook and copy the table.

| Switch A | Switch B | Sweet dispensed? |
|----------|----------|------------------|
| 0 | 0 | |
| 0 | 1 | |
| 1 | 0 | |
| 1 | 1 | |

**A** First build your control system. Turn back to page 12 if you have forgotten how to use the power link.

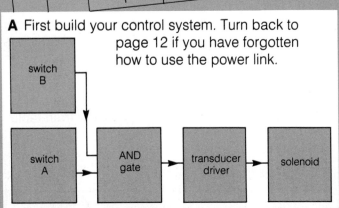

**B** As you did with the OR gate on page 12, press the switches and fill in the truth-table.
Remember: 1 = yes, or on
0 = no, or off

You should notice that you only get a sweet if switch A **and** switch B are pressed together.

An AND gate only works if both inputs are on.

**C** Now let's change one of the switches for a light sensor (and its remote sensor unit).

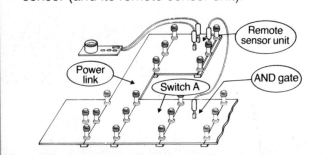

Remember the light sensor is on when light shines on it and off when it is in darkness. Can you work out how your control system will work?

You should be able to adjust your control system so that it gives a Smartie only if you press switch A **and** if it is daylight. (You may have to adjust the control on the remote sensor unit – see page 9.) If you cover up the light sensor (to make it "night-time") it should not give any Smarties even if you press the switch.

**Q13** In your book, draw an AND gate control system for your sweet dispenser with a switch and a reed switch (magnetic switch) as the inputs. What would you have to do to get a sweet?

This is a sort of security system for your sweet dispenser because a magnet has to be put in place before you can get a sweet. If you have time build the system and try it out.

**Q14** What uses can you think of for AND gate control systems? Make a list in your book.

# Information: Making logical decisions

More than a hundred years ago an Irish mathematician, named George Boole, made a study about the way that humans make decisions. He realised that we use three basic thought processes called AND, OR and NOT.

When we make a decision we think about the different statements which can affect our decision. As long as we can say a definite yes or no to each statement we can arrive at a definite (or **logical**) decision.

For example, here is the thought process we go through when we get ready to go out. It is written in the form of a truth-table:

| Is it raining? | Will I be walking? | Wear a raincoat |
|---|---|---|
| No | No | No |
| No | Yes | No |
| Yes | No | No |
| Yes | Yes | Yes |

The truth-table tells you that you only need a raincoat if it is raining AND if you have to walk.

Boole had no idea when he made his study that his ideas would be used more than a hundred years later to design electronic circuits.

This is how an electronic engineer designs a **logic circuit** for a simple burglar alarm system in a house. The engineer has decided to put a hidden switch on a door and use a master switch to turn the burglar alarm system on and off.

**First** the engineer draws a truth-table.

| Is the master switch on? | Is the door open? | Sound the alarm |
|---|---|---|
| No | No | No |
| No | Yes | No |
| Yes | No | No |
| Yes | Yes | Yes |

**Next** the engineer looks at the truth-table to see when the alarm should sound.

The alarm should sound when the master switch is on AND the door is open.

**Then** the engineer draws the logic circuit.

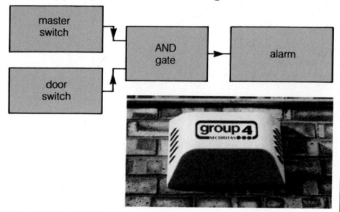

The picture shows a pedestal drill. For safety, the drill will only work if it is switched on and the drill guard is in place.

**Q15** In your book put the heading "making logical decisions" and draw the truth-table for the control system of the drill. Then draw the logic circuit for it.

**3** Controlling your sweet dispenser

# Mini Project 2: Credit card

**Apparatus**
6 V battery (or power supply)    your sweet dispenser    Smarties
3 connecting wires    7 connecting strips    card    scissors
sticky tape    small magnet
Control boards: battery connector (or power supply regulator),
2 remote sensor units, reed switch, light sensor, AND gate,
power link, transducer driver

Now is the time to make use of more of the ideas you have discovered.
Let's see if you can make your sweet dispenser respond to a "credit
card". (But only yours, not somebody else's — otherwise you will find
your Smarties disappearing!)

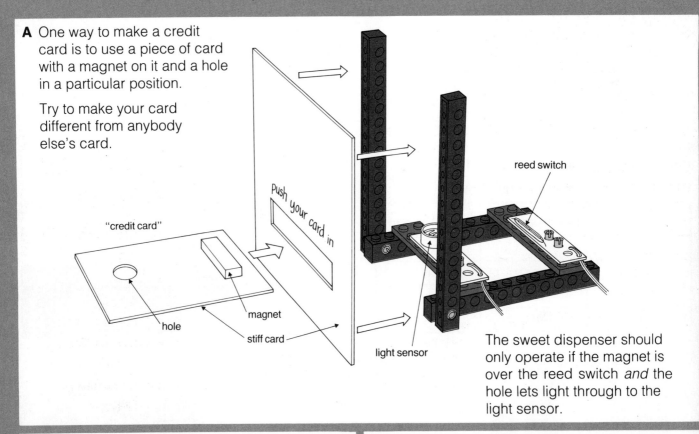

**A** One way to make a credit
card is to use a piece of card
with a magnet on it and a hole
in a particular position.

Try to make your card
different from anybody
else's card.

"credit card"

hole

stiff card

magnet

Push your card in

reed switch

light sensor

The sweet dispenser should
only operate if the magnet is
over the reed switch *and* the
hole lets light through to the
light sensor.

**B** If you use this idea you will need two remote
sensor units, one for the reed switch and one
for the light sensor.

Will you need an AND gate or an OR gate? The
control systems on pages 12 and 14 should
help you if you get stuck.

**C** Work out your control system in your book
before you build it.

Make notes of each step as you build your
project.

# Information: Cash dispensers

Many people are finding cash dispensers very useful for withdrawing money from their bank accounts. They don't have to queue up at the bank counter and they can use the dispenser most hours of the day seven days a week, not just when the bank is open.

To use a cash dispenser you need two things: your cash card, and your **personal identification number (PIN)** known only to you. You put the cash card in the slot and then tap out your number.

The cash card has a magnetic strip on it which is coded magnetically (this is something like the way music is coded onto cassette tape). Inside the dispenser, magnetic sensors recognise the card from its code. The cash dispenser will only dispense money to you if the code on the card matches up with the number you have tapped in.

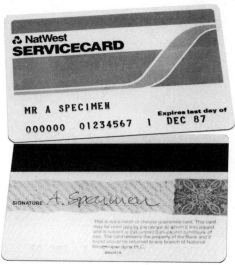

In this way if you lose your card nobody else can use it because they don't know your PIN.

Most cash dispensers allow you to withdraw up to £100 (as long as you have enough money in your account). Because each cash dispenser is linked to the bank's central computer, you can check the balance in your account from any of the bank's cash dispensers. You can even order a cheque book and a statement.

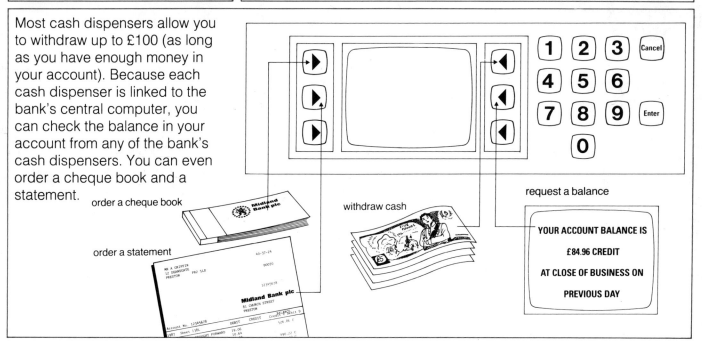

order a cheque book

order a statement

withdraw cash

request a balance

YOUR ACCOUNT BALANCE IS

£84.96 CREDIT

AT CLOSE OF BUSINESS ON

PREVIOUS DAY

**Q16** What advantages are there in using cash dispensers?

**Q17** If you lose your card, what prevents somebody else using your card to get money from the cash dispenser?

**Q18** Why is it very unwise to keep your personal identification number with your cash card?

# Pulse generator

### Apparatus
6 V battery (or power supply)    your sweet dispenser    Smarties
3 connecting wires    7 connecting strips
Control boards: battery connector (or power supply regulator),
buzzer, pulse generator, AND gate, OR gate, power link,
transducer driver, switch unit

If you wanted to dispense ten Smarties it would be tedious having to
press a button ten times. In this experiment, you can build a control
system which will give you a number of Smarties from one press of a
button.

**A** First of all let's find out what a pulse
generator does.
Build this system.

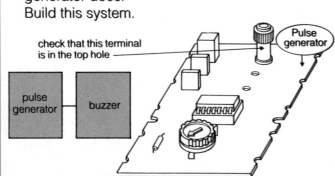

**B** Try adjusting the control on the pulse generator.
Which way do you turn it for the slowest pulse
rate?

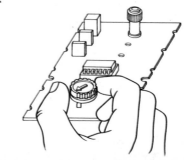

**C** Now build a different control system.

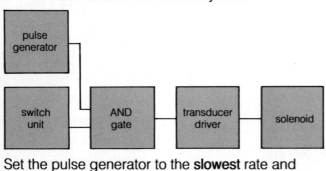

Set the pulse generator to the **slowest** rate and
try pressing the switch.

**D** Next try changing the AND gate for an OR gate.

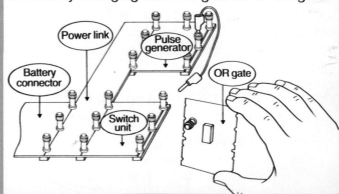

Write the heading "Pulse generator" and draw the first control
system (pulse generator and buzzer). Say what the buzzer does.

**Q19** Suppose you connected a motor to a pulse generator (using a
transducer driver to connect it). What would happen? What would
happen if you turned up the control on the pulse generator?

**Q20** What was different in the way the sweet dispenser operated when
you changed the AND gate for an OR gate?

# 4 Electronic counting

## Counting Smarties

### Apparatus
6V battery (or power supply)    your sweet dispenser    Smarties
2 connecting wires    3 connecting strips
Control boards: battery connector (or power supply regulator),
binary counter and decimal display plugged together,
transducer driver, switch unit, debounced switch unit,
remote sensor unit, light sensor

If you link an electronic counter with your sweet dispenser you will be
able to count Smarties.

**A** First build this system. Make sure that the
slide switches on the counter are moved to
*dec.* and *up* positions. Try pressing the button
and watch the number display carefully. Does
it count properly?

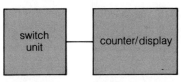

**B** The inside of the
push switch looks
a bit like this:

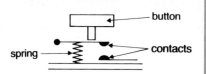

When you push the button the contacts bounce
when they touch. This usually causes more than
one pulse to be sent to the counter.

**C** Now try replacing the switch unit with a
**debounced** switch unit. Watch the display as you
press the button. The debounced switch unit
uses electronics to give just one pulse each time
the button is pressed.

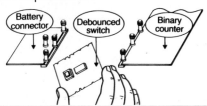

**D** Next replace the debounced switch unit with the
light sensor. Try making it light and dark.

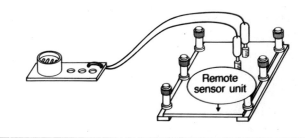

**E** Now let's try counting Smarties.

This system has **two** outputs. One is the solenoid
on your sweet dispenser, the other
is the electronic counter. Look to see
how they are both connected.

Now try your control system
out. Does it work?

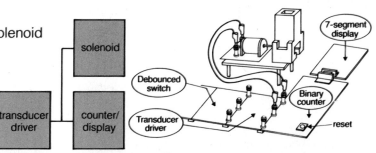

Write the heading "Electronic counting" in your notebook.

**Q1** Draw a diagram of the counter system you
built with a light sensor for the input instead of
a debounced switch.

**Q2** Describe how you would use this system to
count people passing through a doorway.

# Binary counting

### Apparatus

6 V battery (or power supply)      2 connecting strips
Control boards: battery connector (or power supply regulator),
binary counter and decimal display plugged together,
debounced switch

A lamp can be on or off. Using one lamp you can represent two
numbers: off = 0 and on = 1.

Using several lamps together you can represent much bigger
numbers. This experiment shows you how.

Write the heading "Binary counting" in your notebook and then copy
the table.

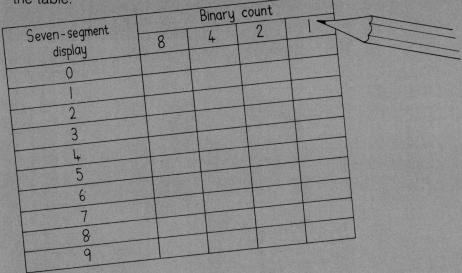

| Seven-segment display | Binary count | | | |
|---|---|---|---|---|
| | 8 | 4 | 2 | 1 |
| 0 | | | | |
| 1 | | | | |
| 2 | | | | |
| 3 | | | | |
| 4 | | | | |
| 5 | | | | |
| 6 | | | | |
| 7 | | | | |
| 8 | | | | |
| 9 | | | | |

**A** First build this system. Make sure you use a
**debounced** switch, and check that the slide
switches are in the *dec.* and *up* positions.

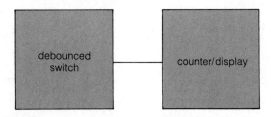

Now press the reset button to set the counter to
zero.

**B** If you look at the binary counter you will see a
row of four terminals numbered 8, 4, 2 and 1.
For each terminal there is an indicator light to
show whether the terminal is on or off.

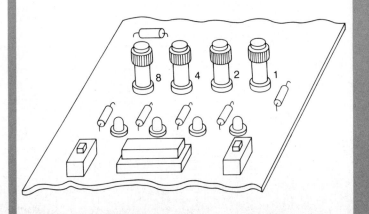

### 4 Electronic counting

**C** Press the debounced switch once and watch the indicator lights on the binary counter. Write the pattern of the lights into your table (remember to write "1" if the light is on and "0" if the light is off).

Keep on pressing the debounced switch and each time write the pattern of lights into your table.

**D** Look at your table carefully. You should be able to see that the binary count shown by the indicator lights is a different way of showing numbers.

Example:

add 4 and 2 together and you get 6

**Q3** Copy the table into your notebook and then fill in the gaps. The first one is done for you.

| Decimal number | Binary number |
|:---:|:---:|
| 2 | 0010 |
| | 1000 |
| | 0101 |
| 1 | |
| 9 | |
| 7 | |

**Q4** What is the biggest number you can show with a binary pattern of three lights?

**Q5** If you had a binary pattern of five lights what number would the fifth light represent?

**4** Electronic counting

# Information: Analogue and digital

There are two different sorts of electrical signal: one is called **analogue** and the other is called **digital**. The difference between the two is something like the difference between the switch and the volume control on a radio. The switch is digital, turning the radio on and off. The volume control is analogue because it adjusts the sound **level**.

Here is an example of showing numbers in an analogue and in a digital way.

This watch is analogue because the hands move smoothly round the face of the watch.

This watch is digital because the display "jumps" as circuits inside the watch switch on and off.

In microelectronics, there are many analogue "chips" but there are far more digital ones. As the use of microelectronics has spread, digital displays have become more and more common. They can be seen in products ranging from weighing machines to petrol pumps.

Sometimes analogue displays are better than digital displays.

For example, a speedometer in a car is analogue. As the speed of the car changes, the needle rises and falls smoothly showing the speed of the car all the time.

The main advantage of digital displays is that the number value can be easily read.

If a digital speedometer were used the numbers would keep jumping. This would be difficult to follow if the speed were changing quickly.

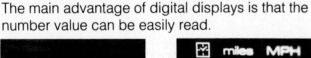

These temperature gauges show this.

Put the heading "Analogue and digital" in your notebook.

**Q6**  Make a list of all the things you can think of which have a digital display.

**Q7**  Draw pictures showing analogue and digital displays on kitchen scales.

**4** Electronic counting

# More about the electronic counter

### Apparatus

6 V battery (or power supply)    1 connecting wire
5 connecting strips
Control boards: battery connector (or power supply regulator),
switch unit, debounced switch, pulse generator, buzzer,
binary counter and decimal display plugged together

You will find the electronic counter very useful in your projects.

In this experiment you can find out how to make the counter reset to
zero automatically. You can also find out how to make the counter
count down instead of up and how to count numbers bigger than ten.

**A** First build this system. The slide switches
should be in the *dec.* and *up* positions.
Make sure you connect the switch unit to the
reset terminal.

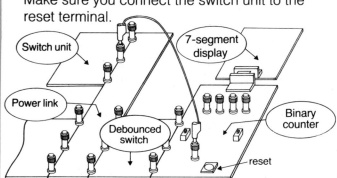

**B** Instead of pressing a switch to make the counter
reset you can make it automatic. Connect a wire
from the reset terminal to number 4 terminal on
the binary counter.

Now keep pressing the
debounced switch.
What happens?

Can you make
the counter
reset at 8?

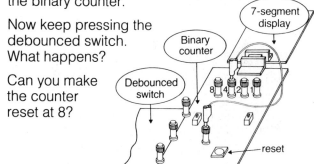

**C** The counter can count down instead of up.

Move the slide switch to the "down" position
and try it out.

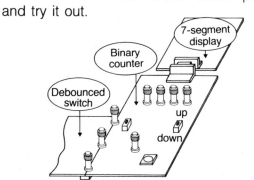

**D** Now move the slide switch back to the *up*
position and build this system.

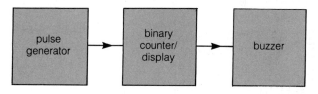

When does the buzzer sound?

Try replacing the buzzer with another counter.
What happens?

Can you make the two counters reset at 40?

**Q8**    How many pulses are needed from the pulse generator to
make the buzzer sound?

**Q9**    Draw this system in your notebook.
How many pulses can this
system count?

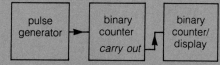

**4** Electronic counting

# Mini Project 3: An "empty" alarm for your sweet dispenser

### Apparatus
6 V battery (or power supply)      your sweet dispenser      Smarties
2 connecting wires      4 connecting strips
Control boards: battery connector (or power supply regulator),
debounced switch, transducer driver, buzzer,
binary counter and decimal display plugged together

You can give your dispenser an alarm which sounds when it is empty.
You use the ideas you learnt on page 23.

Try to work out what this
system will do before you
build it.

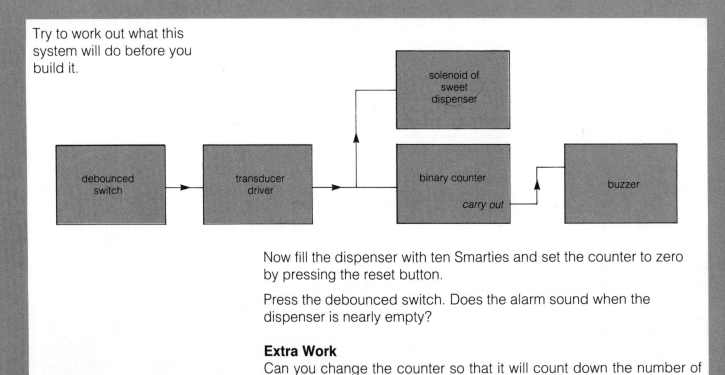

Now fill the dispenser with ten Smarties and set the counter to zero
by pressing the reset button.

Press the debounced switch. Does the alarm sound when the
dispenser is nearly empty?

### Extra Work
Can you change the counter so that it will count down the number of
Smarties left?

**4** Electronic counting

# Information: Seven-segment display

Digital displays are becoming more and more common. The most popular form of display is known as a **seven-segment display**.

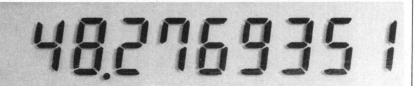

Each figure in a seven-segment display is made up of seven bars (or segments).

There are two common seven-segment displays: one is called **LED** (light emitting diode) and the other is called **liquid crystal**.

seven bars

by making some of the bars show up, any number from 0 to 9 can be displayed

## LED display

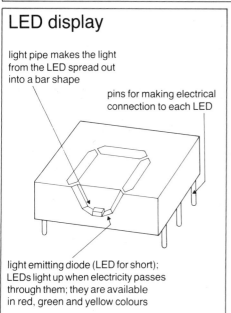

light pipe makes the light from the LED spread out into a bar shape

pins for making electrical connection to each LED

light emitting diode (LED for short); LEDs light up when electricity passes through them; they are available in red, green and yellow colours

## Liquid crystal display

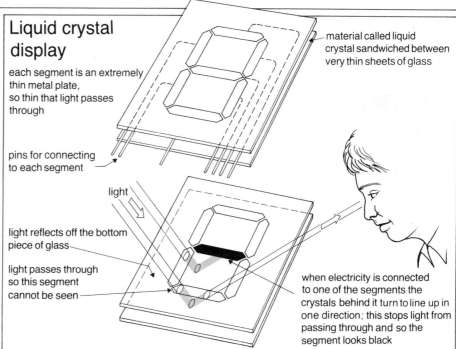

each segment is an extremely thin metal plate, so thin that light passes through

pins for connecting to each segment

light

light reflects off the bottom piece of glass

light passes through so this segment cannot be seen

material called liquid crystal sandwiched between very thin sheets of glass

when electricity is connected to one of the segments the crystals behind it turn to line up in one direction; this stops light from passing through and so the segment looks black

LED displays are bright and show up even if it is dark. Light must shine on a liquid crystal display for the numbers to be seen. In spite of this, liquid crystal displays are becoming more popular than LED displays, particularly in equipment like watches and calculators. This is because liquid crystal displays need much less electricity to make them work and so batteries last longer.

**Q10** See how many letters of the alphabet you can write using a seven-segment display. How much of your name can you write?

**Q11** What is the advantage of using liquid crystal displays instead of LED displays? What is the disadvantage?

**4** Electronic counting

# Stopping the counter

### Apparatus
6 V battery (or power supply)     4 connecting wires
9 connecting strips
Control boards: battery connector (or power supply regulator),
pulse generator, OR gate, AND gate, switch unit, 2 power links,
binary counter and decimal display plugged together

As you will see in the next mini project, it can be useful to make the
counter stop automatically when it reaches a certain number. This
experiment shows you the way to do it.

**A** First, build this system. Make sure that the slide switches are in the *dec.* and *up* positions.
The pictures will help you.

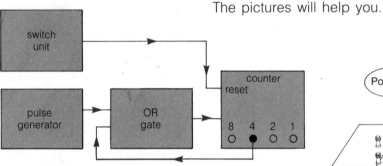

Now reset the counter to zero and watch the
counter. Did it stop counting?

Can you work out why it stops counting when it reaches 4?
Can you make it stop counting when it reaches 8?

**B** Now change the system. It looks a bit complicated
but the picture will help you.

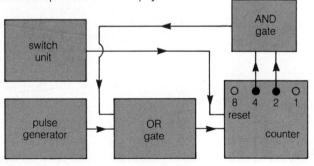

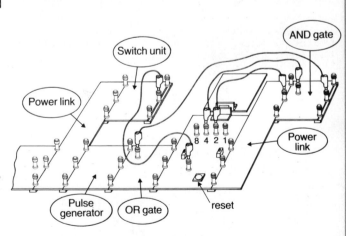

As before, reset the counter and
watch the counter.

Why does it stop counting at 6?

**Q12** Put the heading "Stop counting" and then design and draw a
counting system which will stop counting when it reaches 2.

**4** Electronic counting

# Mini Project 4: Push a button once and get two sweets

### Apparatus
6 V battery (or power supply)    your sweet dispenser    Smarties
6 connecting wires    10 connecting strips
Control boards: battery connector (or power supply regulator),
pulse generator, OR gate, AND gate, 2 power links, switch unit,
binary counter and decimal display plugged together,
transducer driver

Now that you know how to make the counter stop automatically, you
can get your dispenser to give you two sweets by pressing a button
just once.

**A** Remember, the solenoid on your sweet dispenser needs a
transducer driver to make it work. This means that the control
system on page 26 has to be changed slightly for this project.
It looks like this.

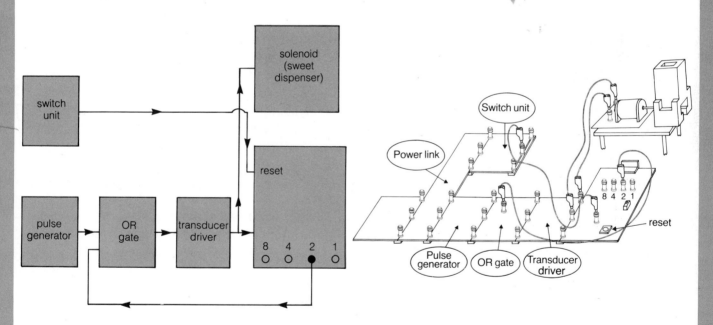

Now press the switch unit.
How many sweets did you get?

**B** You can change the system:
   **a)** Can you make it give you four sweets each time?
   **b)** This is more difficult, but can you get three sweets
each time?

Put the heading "Mini-project 4" in your notebook and
draw your control systems before you build them.

# 5 Projects

## What to do

### Apparatus
LEGO Technical Functions Kit No. 1032 and other LEGO parts if required · 6 V battery (or power supply) · connecting wires · set of control boards · card, scissors, plasticine, sticky tape, etc.

Now that you have finished the experiments you can build your own project.

You have learnt enough in this book for you to attempt any of the projects on the next few pages. If you wish, you could build a different project altogether, but discuss this with your teacher before you start.

**A** Choose one of the four projects on the next four pages.

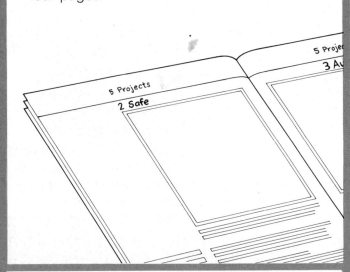

**B** Look at the problem and think how you will solve it. Decide what equipment you will need.

**C** Draw diagrams to work out how to solve some of the problems.

**D** Start building the model. Keep a record of your work in your notebook.

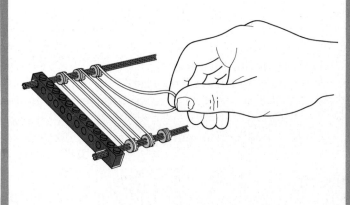

# 1 Automatic fish-food dispenser

An automatic fish-food dispenser would be useful when people are away from home. However, it must be reliable otherwise fish might die. They can die from over-eating as well as from being starved.

**Some ideas to get you started**

You could use your sweet dispenser to dispense the fish food pellets.

Fish food could be in the form of pellets like slices of chalk.

Fish need feeding each day: could you detect nightfall or dawn with a light sensor?

You might want to give more than one pellet at each feeding. Can you build the control system so that you can adjust the number of pellets given at each feeding?

You might want an alarm if the dispenser is low on food.

# 2 Safe

Build a safe and challenge your friends to open the door without sounding the alarm.

**Some ideas to get you started**

You could use the solenoid fitted to the inside of the door to act as a door bolt.

You could use the buzzer as an alarm.

To open the door:
– you might have secret switches
– you might have to choose the right switches to press
– you might need a credit card
– you might have to flash a light
– you might have to press a button a number of times.

## 3  Automatic sorter

> Build a system which will reject boxes which are too tall and then count the number of rejects.

**Some ideas to get you started**

You could use matchboxes for the boxes.

You could make a simple conveyor belt (like the one on pages 10 and 11) to carry the boxes.

You could use a light sensor to detect the boxes – what height will you set it to?

You could use the solenoid as a pusher to knock off the boxes.
If you find this easy, you could try to build a new control system where short boxes are rejected. (**Hint**: you will need two light sensors.)

32

**5** Projects

# 4 Recording the activity of living creatures

Find out how active gerbils (or mice, hamsters or even people) are.

**Some ideas to get you started**

You could make a passageway in the cage with a light beam across it (or somewhere in the classroom if you are recording movement of people).

You could count the number of times the light beam is broken.

You could make the counter only work in daytime or nightime to find out if there is more activity at night.